A SKETCHBOOK FOR VIOLIN

MICHAEL ROSE

THE ASSOCIATED BOARD OF
THE ROYAL SCHOOLS OF MUSIC

1 MARCH

MICHAEL ROSE

2 REVERIE

3 SCOTS AIR

8

4 RUMBA

Moderato, piacevole (♩ = 60)

5 NOCTURNE

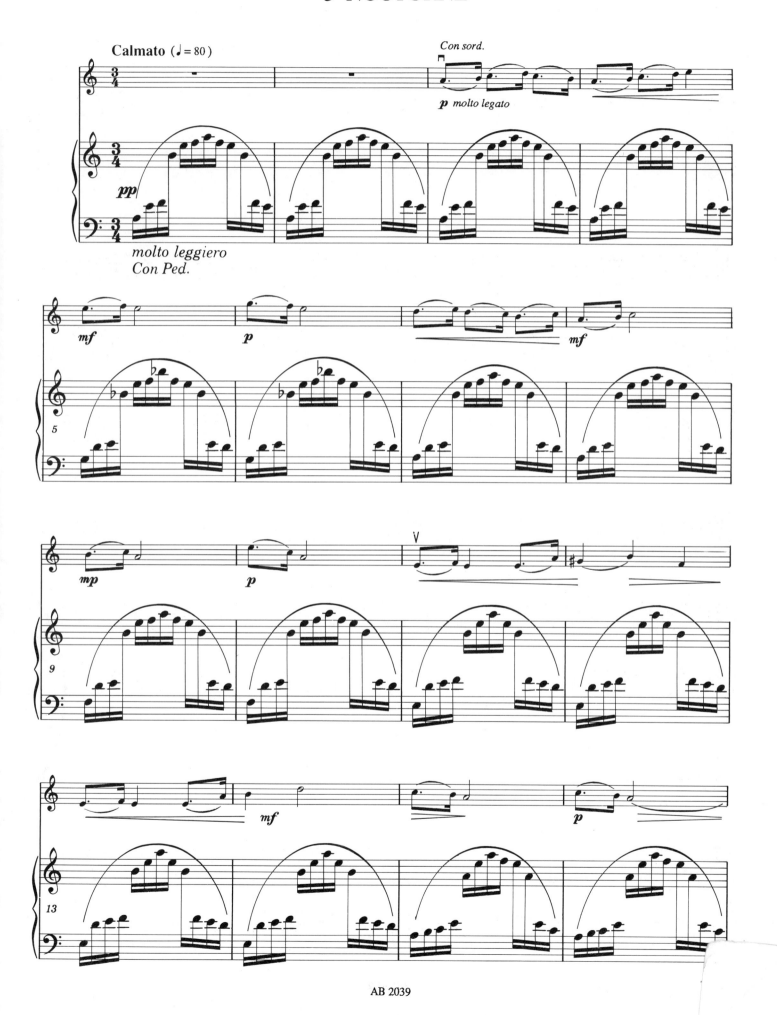

14

6 BURLESQUE

Printed in England by Caligraving Limited Thetford Norfolk

2:89